This book belongs

Wit and Wisdom of
AKBAR and BIRBAL

CONTENT

© 2008 **SHREE** BOOK CENTRE

Printed in India

Mahesh Das becomes Birbal

A young man called Mahesh Das was invited to the court of Akbar. When Mahesh reached the gates of the Royal Palace, he was refused entry by the guard. Mahesh reasoned with the guard to let him into the palace.

Finally the guard relented. But only on the condition that Mahesh would share half of what the emperor gifted him. The greedy guard knew that Emperor Akbar was very generous and always gave money and expensive gifts to visitors.

Mahesh had no choice but to accept the guards terms. He agreed. The guard then allowed him to enter the palace. Mahesh saluted Emperor Akbar respectfully. For the next few hours, Mahesh then entertained the court with amusing stories and witty tales.

Emperor Akbar and his ministers were very impressed by young Mahesh Das, and wanted to show their appreciation. Akbar applauded the young boy and told him that he could have any gift he wanted. All he had to do was ask.

Rather than asking for money and jewels, Mahesh Das surprised everyone by requesting something very unusual. He asked for 50 lashes of the whip. Everyone in the court gasped at Mahesh's request. The emperor too was taken aback at the boy's choice of gift.

Akbar was curious to know the reason for this strange request. When he asked Mahesh Das to explain himself, the young boy told Emperor Akbar about the greedy guard who stood at the gate and his condition for letting him into the palace to meet the emperor.

Akbar was outraged at his guard's behaviour. He called for the Chief of Guards and had the culprit thrown into prison immediately. Akbar was also tremendously impressed with Mahesh's intelligence. He invited Mahesh to remain in his court as one of his courtiers.

The young Mahesh Das accepted the emperor's offer and stayed on in the court. But he was no longer known as Mahesh Das. He was given a new title, Birbal. He became famous in history for being Akbar's most loyal and wise courtier.

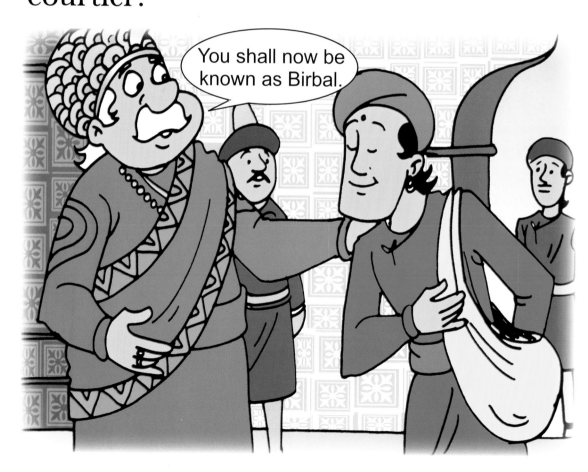

A sweet punishment

One day in court, Emperor Akbar decided to test all his courtiers and his loyal ministers. So he asked them a very strange and challenging question. The emperor promised to reward the person who gave him the cleverest answer.

There was a long silence as the loyal courtiers and ministers waited eagerly for the emperor's question. Akbar then asked the members of his court to decide what punishment should be given to a person who dared to pull his moustache.

The question made everyone in court fall into a shocked silence. Then one agitated minister said the culprit ought to be severely punished. The other ministers also joined in and agreed with him. They also started discussing different kinds of punishment.

Only Birbal who stood all by himself, was smiling. He seemed to be quite amused at the thought of someone pulling the emperor's moustache. Akbar noticed Birbal smiling. He knew that Birbal was very clever, and was eager to know what Birbal would say.

The ministers in the court stopped chattering, and waited for Birbal to reply. Birbal then came forward and said that any person who dared to pull Akbar's moustache should not be punished but must be treated very gently and lovingly.

The ministers present in the court were surprised at Birbal's nerve. They were sure that Akbar would be very angry and punish Birbal for his disrespectful suggestion. But Emperor Akbar was smiling in amusement at Birbal. He asked his loyal minister to explain himself.

Birbal said that no ordinary person present here or in his kingdom would dare to insult the emperor of Delhi, in such a manner. He exclaimed, "Maharaj, the only one who would dare to pull your moustache would be your little grandson who loves you too much to disrespect you!"

The silent court was filled with a loud applause by the ministers. All the courtiers present there were very impressed with Birbal's clever answer. Especially Emperor Akbar, who patted Birbal on the back and gave him a huge and worthy reward.

Why is the camel's neck crooked?

Birbal was the most witty and intelligent courtier in Emperor Akbar's court. One day the emperor was in a good mood and promised to reward Birbal with many gifts for being a loyal advisor and a faithful minister in his kingdom.

Many days passed and Emperor Akbar became very busy with matters of his kingdom and other official work. He forgot about the grand reward he had promised Birbal for his loyal services. Birbal was upset by this but he did not say anything to Akbar.

A few months later, Akbar and Birbal were riding through the kingdom. On their way through a village, they noticed a herd of camels passing along the other side of the road. As they watched the camels go by, Akbar noticed that camels have a crooked neck.

Akbar decided to ask Birbal for an answer. The witty Birbal thought for a while over the strange question. He suddenly realized this was a good chance to remind the emperor of his promise of presenting him with lavish gifts. The promise he had made months ago, but had now forgotten.

The clever Birbal then told Emperor Akbar that the camel had once forgotten an important promise he had made to someone. According to the Holy Scriptures, anyone human or animal who forgot their promise would be cursed with a crooked neck.

The emperor immediately understood what his wise minister was trying to say. He realized that he had forgotten his promise to reward Birbal, and felt very sad about it. He knew he had to make it up to Birbal, and fulfil the promise he had made in court months ago.

When they returned to the palace that evening the emperor immediately ordered his courtiers to bring gold and other gifts from his treasury. He then invited Birbal to the court and showered his loyal minister with wonderful gifts, just like he said he would.

Birbal was very happy that the emperor had finally given him his promised reward. Emperor Akbar felt really sorry that he had forgotten to gift Birbal so he personally came forward to bestow the gifts on his loyal minister. Don't you think that Birbal was a very clever man?

Birbal shortens the Road

Emperor Akbar along with Birbal and his other courtiers, was travelling to a neighbouring kingdom on some important work. The journey by carriage was very long. After a few hours, Akbar grew tired. He was also very bored.

Akbar turned to his fellow travellers with a very strange request. He first remarked that it was such a long road. He then asked if any of them could shorten the road that they were travelling, so they could all reach their destination faster.

The courtiers were puzzled. They pondered for a long time over the request made by Akbar, but none of them could think of a way to shorten the road for the emperor. They were completely baffled by the question put forward to them. It seemed to be an impossible task.

As usual, clever Birbal thought of a solution. He gave the emperor a confident smile and told him that he could indeed make the lengthy road shorter. Akbar was surprised by Birbal's answer and was very interested to know exactly what Birbal had in mind.

For the rest of the journey, Birbal sat beside Emperor Akbar. He started telling him an interesting story. Birbal narrated a very exciting tale about a brave and adventurous king of a small kingdom who had dreams to conquer the whole world.

Emperor Akbar began to enjoy the story so much, that he completely forgot about the long journey. All he could think of was the fascinating story of the valiant king. Even Akbar's courtiers were listening attentively to Birbal, and were keen to hear more.

When Birbal had finished telling the story, Akbar and his courtiers arrived at their destination. Akbar was surprised that they had reached so fast. The emperor's journey had passed quickly because he was listening to an interesting story, and had lost track of time.

Emperor Akbar was very pleased with his favourite minister Birbal. When they started the journey back home, he requested Birbal to narrate another exciting story about the brave king. Birbal did so and their journey home passed just as fast.

The green horse

One summer evening Akbar and Birbal were sitting on a bench in the royal gardens. Akbar had an unusual request. He told Birbal that he had always wanted a green horse, and ordered Birbal to find such a horse within seven days or go to jail.

Birbal smiled to himself and realized that this was just one of the emperor's tests. Both Birbal and the emperor knew that there was no such thing as a green horse, any where in this world. But Birbal respectfully accepted Akbar's task of finding a green horse.

Akbar was impressed with himself. He was always looking for an opportunity to outwit Birbal. But Birbal was a very clever man and it was almost impossible for anyone to get the better of him. This time Emperor Akbar was sure he had succeeded.

Emperor Akbar was sure that he had found a way to trick Birbal because there was no way Birbal could find a green horse. It was an impossible task. But Birbal came back seven days later. He found the emperor sitting in his favourite bench in the garden.

Birbal announced that for the past seven days he searched all over the kingdom and in the neighbouring kingdoms too and finally was able to find a green horse as desired by the emperor. On hearing this Akbar was quite startled. He looked puzzled at Birbal.

Birbal told Akbar that he had found a green horse and that the owner of the green horse was willing to sell the animal. But he would do so only if Akbar would accept two conditions without asking any sort of questions. Akbar was intrigued.

Birbal laid down the owner's conditions. The first condition was that Emperor Akbar himself should go to collect the green horse. The second condition was that the emperor was to collect the horse on a day that was not one of the days in the week. Akbar was baffled by these conditions.

Akbar realized that finding a day that was not in the week was as impossible as finding a green horse. Birbal had found out a wonderful way to trick him. Once again, Akbar had to accept that Birbal had proved himself a wise and witty minister.

How many crows in the Kingdom

It was a beautiful morning in Akbar's kingdom. So he decided to take a walk in his royal gardens with his trusted courtier Birbal. While they were admiring the colourful flowers, Akbar noticed that there were quite a few crows flying about.

Now Emperor Akbar knew that no one would be able to count exactly how many crows there were in his kingdom, it was an impossible task. But he realized this was a good opportunity to test Birbal's wisdom. Akbar asked Birbal how many crows were there in his kingdom.

Birbal at once realized that the emperor was testing him once again. He looked up at the sky, the trees and all around him and thought for a moment. Then he started to smile to himself as he had found a way to answer Emperor Akbar's question.

Akbar was greatly impressed by Birbal's quick reply. At the same time he was a little disappointed that Birbal had thought of a reply so quickly. So, he decided to try once again to outsmart Birbal. He pondered for a while and then again asked Birbal a question.

Akbar then asked Birbal what would happen if there were more crows than Birbal had counted. He was confident that there was no way that the witty Birbal could answer this question. But Birbal was prepared with an answer to the question.

Waving his hand at the crows around him in the garden Birbal replied that if there were more crows in the kingdom, then it was only because crows from the neighbouring kingdoms had come to visit their relatives here so they were the guest crows .

Akbar was amused by Birbal's reply. Still, he was not fully satisfied. He wanted to test Birbal further and so he asked Birbal another question. What would happen if they counted fewer crows than the number Birbal had said?

Once again, Birbal answered without hesitation. He said that if there were fewer than ninety-five thousand four hundred and sixty-three crows, then it was only because the crows from here had gone to visit their friends and relatives in other kingdoms.

Better than Birbal

Emperor Akbar was very fond of the witty Birbal. This made two of his courtiers very jealous. So they thought of a plan of how to please Akbar so that Akbar would favour them as much as he favoured Birbal.

The two courtiers went up to emperor Akbar's chamber in private and claimed that they could do anything that Birbal could do and that they were as clever as Birbal. The courtiers offered to carry out any task that the emperor assigned to them.

Akbar was amused by this request made by his jealous courtiers. So he gave the courtiers a task each. If they could complete these tasks successfully, Akbar promised to proclaim in court and all over the kingdom that they were his most intelligent courtiers and that they were better than Birbal.

Akbar asked the first courtier to bring him fire wrapped in a paper. His task for the second courtier was to bring him air wrapped in a paper. He warned the courtiers that if they failed to complete their tasks, they would be thrown in jail.

The courtiers were completely taken aback, but accepted the tasks which the emperor assigned them because they had no choice. For days they tried many different ways, performed many experiments with paper but could not do what Akbar has asked them to do.

The courtiers pondered night and day but failed to come up with any solution. And now, their time was running out. They were very worried, as they had only one week to prove themselves. Both the courtiers knew that only one person could help them with their tasks.

When Birbal heard of Akbar's tasks he promised to help the courtiers. He told the first courtier to take a paper lantern to Akbar. He told the second courtier to take a paper fan. The courtiers did as Birbal had advised them.

Emperor Akbar immediately realized that Birbal had helped the two courtiers. But he forgave them and did not send them to jail. After that day, the two courtiers never said a bad word against Birbal again. They had learnt their lesson, and knew that Birbal deserved to be the favourite minister in court.

The poor man's dream

A poor worker in Akbar's kingdom was very proud that inspite of his small salary he had never been in debt. One night he dreamt that he had borrowed money from the moneylender. When he woke up in the morning he told his wife about his dream.

Somehow, the moneylender found out about the poor worker's dream. He was a wicked man. He went to the worker's house and demanded repayment for the money, even though it was in a dream. The poor worker did not know what to do.

The poor worker went straight to Birbal's house and begged for his help. Birbal listened patiently to the man's problem and promised to help him deal with the greedy moneylender. Birbal then thought of a plan. He summoned the greedy moneylender to his house.

Birbal placed some gold coins on a table with a mirror in front of the pile of coins. When the moneylender reached Birbal's house, he was invited to the inner room. When he entered the room, he saw the gold and his eyes started shining. He thought that his evil plan had worked.

The wise Birbal told the moneylender that the gold in front of him was the repayment for the money borrowed by the worker in his dream. As soon as he heard this the greedy moneylender rushed across the room and immediately reached for the coins. But Birbal stopped him.

Then, Birbal explained to the greedy moneylender that since he had lent the worker the gold coins only in a dream and not in reality, he was only entitled to the reflection of the gold coins in the mirror and not the real coins on the table.

The wicked moneylender knew that Birbal had outwitted him. He was ashamed of himself and he apologized immediately to Birbal and the worker and he also promised to give up his evil ways. Saying this the moneylender departed from Birbal's house, a changed person.

The poor worker was very relieved that he did not have to repay the moneylender any money. He praised Birbal's wisdom, and thanked him a thousand times for his invaluable help. Birbal was indeed a wise person who helped anyone in need.

Straw in the beard

One morning in court, Emperor Akbar decided to have a little fun with his favourite minister Birbal. He took off his royal signet ring and gave it to one of his other courtiers secretly before Birbal could arrive in court. He then summoned Birbal.

Akbar told Birbal that he had misplaced his royal signet ring which was very precious. He said that all the other courtiers had looked for it , but could not find it. He pretended to be very unhappy and upset about it and ordered Birbal to find it as soon as possible.

Clever Birbal realised that Akbar was just testing him. He knew that the emperor was always finding ways to try and outwit him but it was all in jest and not seriously. Of course Birbal always found a way to solve all of Akbar's surprise tests.

Birbal knew that Akbar had been busy with official work in court all day. He realized that the ring had to be hidden with one of the courtiers present in court. All he had to do was find out which courtier the emperor had entrusted his ring to.

Birbal went back to his seat, and quietly devised a plan to reveal who was holding the signet ring. In the meantime, Akbar continued to pretend that he was upset over the loss of his precious ring that his wife had gifted him. She too would be very upset, he told Birbal.

When Birbal was ready with his answer he came up in front and told Akbar that his ring was in the court itself. And he was very sure that one of Akbar's courtiers present here in court had hidden it and that he knew the identity of this courtier.

Birbal made all the courtiers stand before him and he looked searchingly at all of them. Finally he claimed that the man who has the emperor's ring had a straw in his beard. The courtier with the ring unconsciously stroked his beard to check for the straw.

Birbal correctly identified the courtier who had put his hand up to check his beard. The courtier returned the signet ring to Akbar. Akbar and all his courtiers were amazed at Birbal's intelligence. Emperor Akbar realized that it was nearly impossible to outwit Birbal.

Birbal outwits a cheat

One day in the kingdom of Emperor Akbar there lived a farmer called Ram. He and his neighbour Shyam had a disagreement over the price of a well. They argued and argued for days, but could not settle the matter by themselves.

The next day, both Ram and Shyam went to Birbal's home, because they were desperate for a solution. It was well known in the kingdom that Birbal was wise and fair in his judgment. Ram was confident that Birbal would help them resolve the matter.

Ram told Birbal that he had bought a well from Shyam his neighbour for a fair price. Now, Shyam was demanding payment for the water in the well too. Ram added that he could not afford to pay any more money.

Then Shyam made his argument that he had only agreed to sell the well to Ram, and not the water in it. He smartly added hence, his demand was just and it was only right that Ram should pay him extra to use the water in the well.

After they had put their arguments before Birbal both Ram and Shyam waited eagerly while Birbal thought over the matter for a moment. It was obvious to the wise Birbal that Shyam was trying to trick Ram into paying him more money.

Birbal pondered over the problem. He felt sorry for Ram the poor farmer. Birbal did not like cheats like Shyam. He had to do something. He thought quickly of a clever solution that would teach the crooked farmer a lesson he would never forget.

Birbal said that the well belonged to Ram and there was no doubt about it. If Shyam claimed that the water belonged to him, it was only fair that he should pay rent to Ram for taking care of his water. After all, he was storing his water in Ram's well.

The crook Shyam, realized that Birbal had very smartly outwitted him. He was very embarrassed. He apologized humbly to Ram and to Birbal and walked away in shame. Ram was so happy that he fell at Birbal's feet in gratitude.

The emperor's parrot

Emperor Akbar was very fond of animals and birds. He was once gifted an exotic and beautiful parrot by the king of a foreign land. The bright green bird was very clever and was trained to talk. He entertained Akbar all the time.

The king loved the parrot very much and kept him under special care. He hired the services of a bird trainer to take care of the parrot. He was so protective of his parrot that he threatened to hang the person who informed him of the parrot's death.

Sadly, one summer evening due to some strange illness the parrot fell sick and died. The next morning when the bird trainer came in to feed the bird he found it dead. The servant was terrified of telling Akbar the sad news. He remembered Akbar's threat and feared that he would be hanged.

The scared servant knew that only one person could help him. He ran as fast as he could to Birbal's house. The servant rushed into Birbal's chamber and fell at his feet. The bird trainer was in tears he begged Birbal to find a solution to his problem.

Birbal felt sorry for the poor man. He reassured the servant, that he had nothing to worry about. Nothing would happen to him. He sent the worried bird trainer back to work and he himself decided to announce to the emperor the sad death of his favourite parrot.

When Birbal reached Akbar's court he found him seated in the balcony. Birbal approached the emperor very slowly and stammered, "Sire… your… your parrot…" Akbar was instantly suspicious by Birbal's behaviour and asked him what had happened to his dear parrot.

Birbal informed Akbar that his parrot was not eating or drinking anything. He said that the parrot was not opening his eyes, or moving his feathers or even speaking. Akbar immediately asked, "Is the parrot dead?"

Birbal didn't say a word but just nodded his head indicating 'yes'. Akbar immediately understood why Birbal had informed him in this manner. Akbar was very upset about the death of his parrot, but he did not hang anyone, thanks to Birbal.

Birbal goes to heaven

Emperor Akbar's barber was very jealous of Birbal. "I know how to get rid of Birbal", the wicked Barber thought to himself. One day while giving the emperor a shave, the barber said to Akbar "Jahanpanah, I met your father in my dreams".

"How is my father doing in heaven?" asked a very surprised Emperor Akbar. The cunning barber who was waiting for this chance, replied, "He is happy, Sire, but he is also very lonely. He would be happier if he had someone to make him laugh and keep him company.

The next day, a worried Emperor Akbar summoned Birbal to his chamber and requested him to go to heaven and keep his father company. Birbal guessed that this was the wicked barber's plan, but he agreed to Akbar's request without saying a word.

Birbal wanted to let Akbar know that the crooked barber had tricked him into believing the story about his father. But first, Birbal had to think of a plan that would save his own life. Then he called his own trusted servants and quickly made some arrangements.

Birbal dug a grave near the emperor's palace, and then he dug a tunnel from the grave to a room inside his own house. He told his servants to keep it a secret. He then went back to Emperor Akbar's palace and informed him that he was ready to go to heaven to serve his father.

"Sire, please bury me alive so that I can be alive when I meet your father," Birbal requested. Akbar readily agreed to his request. Birbal was buried in the grave he had dug. He then crawled through the tunnel and hid in his house for six months.

Six months later, Birbal returned to Akbar's court with long hair and an uncut beard. The emperor was overjoyed to see Birbal. "How is my father?" asked Akbar anxiously. "He is happy, Sire, but like me, he needs a barber as there are no barbers in heaven," replied Birbal.

Suddenly Akbar understood the barber's wicked plan. He immediately ordered his guards to arrest the wicked man and throw him in prison. " You are truly wise, Birbal!" exclaimed Emperor Akbar as he showered him with many gifts.